Laughing Letters

(Revised)

Dr. J. R. Linn • Mabel Bruce

Dorothy Donaldson • Jean Ellis

Anne Saunders • Janet Trischuk

Holt, Rinehart and Winston of Canada, Limited
Toronto • Montreal

ISBN 0-03-924101-7

LANGUAGE PATTERNS
Level One

Tracing Our Letters
Listening Letters (Revised)
Laughing Letters (Revised)
Magic Letters (Revised)
Rainbow Letters
The Reading Box

Working with Letters
Book 1   Book 2
Independent Activities
Diagnostic Tests
Language Patterns
Library One

ACKNOWLEDGEMENTS

Cover Design:
TOM SANKEY

Illustrators:

BARRIE APPLEBY
RUTH BAGSHAW
PHILIP BALSAM
KALMAN BANITZ
VERONIKA BENJAMIN
CHARLES DOLESCH
SUSANNE DOLESCH

JANE H. GOTTARDI
DENNIS NOBLE
BOB SEGUIN
LARRY SERBLOWSKI
STEWART SHERWOOD
KEN STAMPNIK
BOB TERINGO

Every effort has been made to identify the illustrators of the original edition. If any names have been omitted, the publisher humbly apologizes.

Printed in Canada
1 2 3 4 5   80 79 78 77 76

Contents

A Trick 7

Robin's Song 11

The King's Ring 12

The Big Bass 17

Kim 21

Tad 25

Tell Me A Story 29

Gus and the Nuts 30

The Band 34

The Missing Things 35

Just a Puppet 37

Tell Me A Story 42

Fred Frog 43

Brenda 49

Collecting Things 53

Red Hen's Egg 54

Thelma 59

Alan's Pal 62

In the Big Tent 65

Tell Me A Story 71

A Blanket is a Splendid Thing 72

The Twins 73

At the Well 77

Timmy at Camp 80

The Unhappy Bunny 86

Velda 90

Zak Zebra 91

Beth 96

My Wish 100

Tell Me A Story 101

Daffy Duckling 102

The Best Shot 109

The Frisky Wind 113

Chuck's Best Pal 114

A Dandy Lunch 120

Tell Me A Story 127

A Trick

Ron Rabbit has a string.
Kit Cat grabs the string.
Ron Rabbit thinks,
"I am a strong rabbit."

Kit Cat thinks,
"I am a strong cat."

Rick Rat sits in the grass.
The Rat grins.

Kit Cat grabs the string.
Ron Rabbit grabs the string.
The Rat grins.

The Rabbit hangs on to the string.
The Cat hangs on to the string.
Rick Rat thinks, "Ha! A trick!"

The string snaps!
Rick Rat sits in the grass.
The Rat grins.

Robin's Song

A robin is hopping,
Is hopping, is hopping.
A robin is hopping,
Singing his song.

A robin is packing,
Is packing, is packing.
A robin is packing,
Singing his song.

A robin is singing,
Is singing, is singing.
A robin is singing,
Singing his song.

11

The King's Ring

This is the King.

The King hasn't got his ring.
It is not on his hand.

Is it on the mat?

It isn't on the mat.

Is it in the bath?

It isn't in the bath.

This is Kip.
Kip is sitting on the grass.

Ha! Kip has it.
Kip has the ring.

The King has his ring.
The King is not sad.

The Big Bass

Dad is sitting on the sand.

Mom is standing on the dock.

Mom has a rod.

Don is on a rock.

Don has a stick and a string.

A pin is on the string.

Mom grips the rod.
Mom has a bass!

Don sits and sits.
His string bobs.
Don grins.
A bass! A BIG bass!

Don grabs at the bass.
Don is not on the rock.
Don has a bass and a bath.

Kim

Kim is not at a rink.
Kim is at the pond.

Stop! Stop, Kim!
It is not thick.
It's thin! It cracks!

Kim sinks in the pond.
"Scamp, Scamp!" sobs Kim.
Can Kim grab Scamp?

Kim's hand is on Scamp.
Hang on, Kim!

Kim is back.
Mom thanks Scamp.
Mom pats Scamp.

Tad

Tad is a fat frog.
Tad is sitting on a pad.
The pad is his raft.
Tad drifts on his soft raft.

Tad sits and sits on his raft.

A stick skims past Tad.

"That is a fast raft," thinks Tad.

"I can hop onto that raft."

Tad hops off his pad.
Tad hops onto the stick.
It rips. It spins.
Tad isn't on a raft.

Tad hops back onto his pad.
"That stick is a bad raft. It tips.
This pad is a grand raft."
Tad drifts on his raft.

Gus and the Nuts

Ann picks up nuts.

Ann dumps the nuts into a bag.

The bag is fat.

The bag is on the grass.

Grandpa must bring the bag
into the cabin.

Ann is in the cabin.

Gus is sitting.

Gus jumps.

Gus runs to the bag.

Gus grabs a nut from the bag.
Gus runs fast.
The nut is in the trunk.
Gus runs back to the bag.
This is a big job.
Gus runs and runs.

Ann brings Grandpa to the bag.
Grandpa picks it up.
The bag is not fat.
Gus has the nuts.
Gus sits and cracks a big nut.
M-m-m-m!

The Band

Pots and pans,
Gongs and drums:
Sandra hits,
Robin hums.

Tip the hat,
Hit the drum.
Rat, tat, tat.
Rum, tum, tum.

Run and jump.
This is grand.
Thump, thump, thump.
It's a band.

The Missing Things

This is Bud.

Bud has on his cap and mitts.
Bud has his bag, his puck, and his stick.

Bud is sitting at the rink.
Bud is sitting in the hut.
Bud digs into his bag.
Bud dumps his bag.
Bud is frantic. "I must run back.
I must pick up the missing things."

Just a Puppet

Ted is sick in bed.

Ted has the mumps and must rest.

His neck is throbbing.

Ted is sad.

Jed is Ted's dog.
Jed jumps up on Ted's bed.
Ted hugs his dog.

Jed jumps off the bed
and runs to get a puppet.
Back runs Jed bringing a frog puppet.
Ted grins.

Ted thinks, "This puppet can hop.
This puppet can kick."
The frog puppet kicks Jed.

Jed jumps back.
Jed is upset.
Gr, gr, gr!
Ted grins at Jed.
"This is not a frog.
This is just a puppet."

Tell Me A Story

Fred Frog

Ken has a frog.

Ken got it at the pond.

The frog is Fred Frog.

Ken hangs on to him.

Fred Frog can't hop and jump.

"Ken, Ken!"

Ken pops Fred Frog into his pocket.

Ken has hidden Fred from his Mom.

Ken is in bed.

Fred Frog is in his jacket pocket.

Mom Frog jumps up on Ken's bed.
Mom is a big frog.
Mom's skin has bumps and humps.
Mom Frog must get Fred back.
Can Ken run?
This frog is too big.

Ring — ring — ring!
"Ken. Get up!"
Ken jumps up.

Ken gets Fred Frog.
Back to the pond runs Ken.
Ken sets Fred Frog in the sand.
Fred Frog hops into the pond.

Brenda

Brenda has a bus ticket.

Brenda and Jim run.

Jim gasps, "It's the bus!"

Brenda runs to the bus stop.

Brenda jumps onto the bus.
Honk, honk!
Brenda has left on the bus.
Jim is left sitting.

The bus skims along.

A kitten is hidden in the grass.

51

The kitten runs.
Honk! Honk!
Brenda gasps.
The bus stops.

Collecting Things

Jill collects —
Big brass buttons,
Springs from clocks,
String in bits,
Thin, flat rocks,

A stamp from Africa,
A stamp from Japan,
Bus tickets,
And lids from cans;
Tacks, jacks,
And plastic rockets,
Jill collects
In big pockets.

Red Hen's Egg

Brent has a pet.
Brent's pet is Red Hen.

Brent collects eggs from the hens
but hasn't Red Hen's egg.

Nick Skunk is digging at the pen.
The hens panic.
Cluck — cluck — cluck! Cluck, cluck!

Nick Skunk sniffs at the nests
and smells an egg.
It is Red Hen's egg.

Nick licks his lips. Nick tugs at the nest.
The nest slips. It tips.
Splat!
The egg cracks.
Nick Skunk is a mess.

Thelma

Thelma the Camel runs across the sand.

Thelma stops to drink at the spring.

Thelma sniffs at the grass.

M-m-m.

The camel grabs the grass.

Crack! Crack! Thelma stops.

Thelma sobs.

Thelma is at the dentist's.
The dentist can help Thelma.
The dentist drills.
The dentist fills.
Thelma grins.

Thelma runs on the sand.
Thelma drinks from the spring.
At last Thelma has that grass!

Alan's Pal

Alan is sad.

Alan is lost.

Alan sobs and sobs.

This is Alan's pal.
Alan's pal stops.
Alan's pal helps Alan
get back to his Mom and Dad.

Alan hugs his pal.

Mom is glad that Alan is back.

Dad thanks Alan's pal.

In the Big Tent

Jill is in the tent.
Jill is with Dad.

Jill jumps up, "Clowns, Dad! Clowns!"

Into the ring steps Fat Clown.

Fat Clown has red pants.

His jacket is pink.

His hat has a bell.

"Ding, ding," rings the bell.

Then Thin Clown skips into the ring.

Thin Clown has pink pants.

His jacket has big brass buttons.

Thin Clown has a splendid umbrella.

Fat Clown has a big clock.

Bang! The clock splits.

Fat Clown drops flat.

Up jumps Fat Clown and bows.

"I will get a clap too," thinks Thin Clown.
Thin Clown steps onto a plank.

Fat Clown sets a tub on the plank.

Along the plank steps Thin Clown.
Then Thin Clown jumps off the plank.

The plank tips. The tub spills.

Fat Clown gets wet.

His pants and jacket drip.

His red hat drips.

The bell on his hat rings a sad song.

"Dong, dong, dong."

The crowd claps.

Tell Me A Story

A Blanket is a Splendid Thing

A blanket is a splendid thing:
A raft that drifts,
A tent on sand,
A rocket to a distant land.

A blanket is a splendid thing:
A flag that flaps,
A gown that's grand,
A ticket to a distant land.

The Twins

Wilfred is a bug.

Wilma Bug is his twin.

Wilma has a red wagon.

Wilfred is sitting in the wagon.

Wilma Bug is tugging the wagon.

Along the path runs Wilma.

Wilma runs as fast as the wind.

"This is fun," thinks Wilfred.

The wagon hits a rock.
BUMP, bump, BANG!
Wilfred is sitting in the soft mud.
"I am a mess," thinks Wilfred.
"I must get this mud off!"
Wilma helps him.

Wilfred jumps up
into the wagon.
"I'll drag the wagon to the well,"
thinks Wilma.
Along the path runs Wilma
with Wilfred in the wagon.
Wilfred can swim in the well.
It's fun to swim in the well.

At the Well

The twins jump into the well.
The Bugs swim and swim.
"This is fun!" yells Wilma.
"I can swim well."
"Yes, yes," yells Wilfred.
"This is fun."

Wilma sits on the big bucket.

"This is the best spot to rest," yells Wilma.

A fat frog is sitting in the bucket.

The fat frog thinks, "Yum — yum!

I will get that bug."

Just then Wilma jumps off the bucket.

The bucket t
      i
         p
           s!

The frog gets wet.

Wilma Bug grins.

Then the twins run back to the wagon.

Timmy At Camp

Timmy is in the tent.

Timmy is resting on his camp cot.

Tap, tap!

"Is that a fly tapping at my tent?"

Tap, tap, tap!

"Is it a cricket tapping?"

Tap, tap, tap, tap!

"Is it a skunk?"

Timmy lifts the tent flap.

Timmy jumps back. It's a DRAGON!

It's a l^um_py, b_um^py dragon!

Sniff, sniff, sniff.

"Is that dragon crying?" asks Timmy.

"The dragon is sad.

I will help him."

The dragon steps into the tent.
The dragon sobs, "I am lost.
I think my den is across that hill
and along the dusty path."

"I'll get my wagon," thinks Timmy,
"and help the dragon get to his den."
Desmond Dragon hops into the wagon.
Timmy tugs the wagon up the hill.

Then Timmy gets into the wagon
with the dragon.
Down
     down
         down.
Down the hill bumps the wagon.
"Is this the dusty path?" asks Timmy.
"Yes, Timmy. Now I can get to the den
by myself."

The l^um_py, b_um^py dragon

went galloping down the dusty path

to his den.

The Unhappy Bunny

Billy is a bunny.

Billy is an unhappy bunny.

His pal Robby Robin can fly.

Freddy Frog can swim.

Billy cannot fly.

Billy cannot swim.

Billy just hops.

Billy hops along the path.

Billy trips.

Is it a stick?

Billy bends down.

It is an umbrella, a black umbrella.

Billy picks up the umbrella.
Click! The umbrella is up.
The wind puffs. The wind fills
the umbrella and lifts Billy,
up, up, up.

Billy hangs on.

The wind drops.

Down
    drifts
        the
            bunny.

Billy is happy now.

Billy can fly.

Velda

Velda has a velvet dress,
Velvet dress, velvet dress.
Velda has a velvet dress
With pink satin frills.

Velda has a velvet hat,
Velvet hat, velvet hat.
Velda has a velvet hat,
It's as soft as silk.

Velda sings a happy song
Happy song, happy song.
Velda sings a happy song
Swinging on the swing.

Zak Zebra

Zak is a big zebra.

Zak thinks, "I am a grand animal!

The fox is not as grand as I am.

The skunk is not as grand as I am."

Zak gallops to the pond.

"Let's trick that zebra," puffs the wind.

"Yes, let's," grins the sun.

"Let's trick that silly zebra."

Zak drinks and drinks.
Then Zak spots himself in the glassy pond.
Zak thinks, "How grand I am!"

The wind puffs on the pond.
Now the pond is not glassy.

Zak is getting dizzy.

Zak cannot think well.

"How grand... a... zebra... I"

PLOP! Zak sinks into the pond.

The sun winks and the wind grins.

Zak swims frantically.

Zak is too dizzy to get up on the bank.
The animals run to the pond.
The animals must help him.

Zak thanks the animals and quickly runs
into the thicket.
Zak thinks, "I am not a grand zebra.
I am wet and muddy.
How silly a zebra I am."

✓ Beth

Beth is a moth. Beth is in a closet.
"Hm," thinks Beth. "This cloth is yummy.
Velvet cloth is thick. Satin cloth is thin.
This is fun."

Thump! thump! thump!

A hand slips moth pellets into the closet.

Sniff, sniff, sniff.

"This stuff smells! I must fly!"

Beth sobs, "I'm dizzy. My tummy is sick.
I'll rest."
Beth slips into a jacket pocket.
Beth rests in the pocket.
"I'm very ill."
Suddenly a hand grabs the jacket.

Beth sniffs.

Beth thinks, "This smells just grand.

I'm not dizzy. I'm not sick.

I can fly into the sky."

My Wish

I wish I had a fish
Swimming in this dish.
Splash, splash, splash.
Funny, funny fish.

I wish I had a fox
Sitting in this box.
Yip, yip, yip.
Funny, funny fox.

I wish I had a frog,
Sitting on a log.
Glug, glug, glug.
Funny, funny frog.

I wish I had a skunk
Sitting in this trunk.
Sniff, sniff, sniff.
Funny, funny skunk.

I wish I had a duck
Sitting in my truck.
Quack, quack, quack.
Funny, funny duck.

Tell Me A Story

Daffy Duckling

"It's fun to travel," thinks Daffy.

"I wish I had a ship.

I can't swim to the big, big pond.

If I had a big shell . . . If I had a box . . . "

Black Hen thinks, "Silly duckling.

Can't it swim in this pond?

It isn't a big, big pond, but it's wet."

Daffy runs along the bank
still wishing ... "If I had a ship ... "
Daffy's mash is in his dish.
Daffy sniffs the mash.
"Ha!" thinks Daffy. "This dish is a ship."
Daffy dumps the mash.
Daffy drags the dish to the pond.

Daffy jumps into the dish.

"This is fun! Now I will travel."

Daffy flaps his wings and gets

to the big, big pond.

Then Daffy sits and drifts.

A hungry fish swims by.
The fish thinks, "I will get this duck.
The dish will tip and I will get him."

Daffy drifts along.

A ship puffs by.

S l a s h, s p l a s h, s l a s h,
p h, a p h.

Daffy's dish rocks. It upsets.

Daffy is IN the b-i-g, BIG POND!

Daffy swims frantically.

The hungry fish swims too.

"Quack! quack!" yells Daffy. "Help! help!"

It's a long swim.

Daffy cannot stop to rest.

His wings and legs throb.

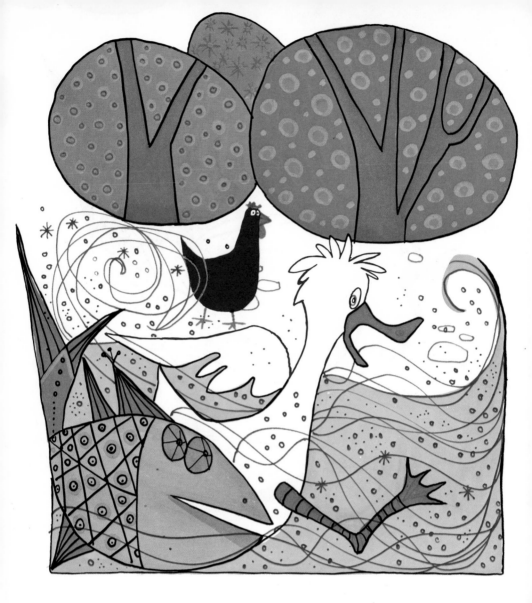

The big fish grabs Daffy's leg.

Daffy yanks it from the fish and swims on.

At last Daffy flops on the bank.

Daffy is dizzy and sick.

Black Hen clucks, "That silly duckling."

The Best Shot

Andy and Dan skim fast
on the rink.
The puck skips past Linda.
"I'll get that puck," Linda thinks.

Whack! The puck hits the plank.

Andy must rush with his stick.

If Linda gets the puck,

Linda is the best shot.

Andy is a flash.

Andy skims down the rink to the puck.

Dan wants to help Andy hit the puck.

Crash! Andy runs into the plank.

Crash! Dan runs into Andy.

Crash! Wham! Andy and Dan hit the rink.

Dan is sitting on Andy's leg.

Linda grabs the puck.
It skips off the plank.
The puck is a flash.
The puck hits the end.
Linda is the best shot.

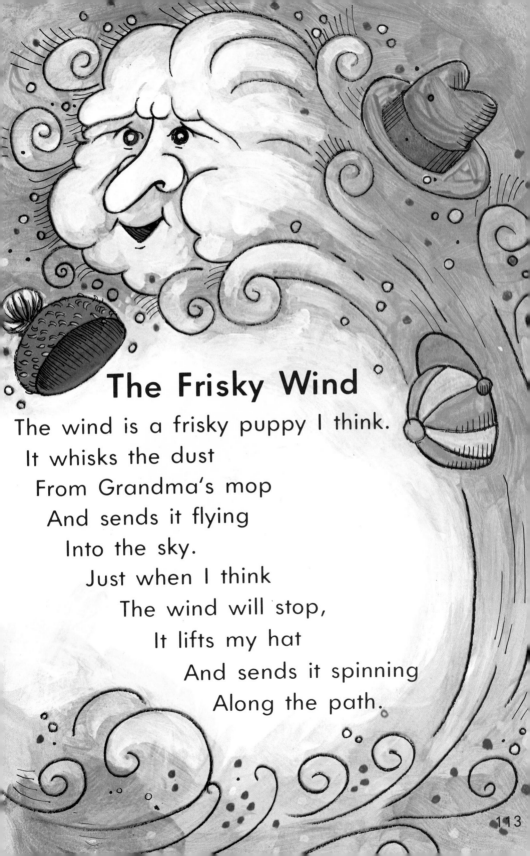

The Frisky Wind

The wind is a frisky puppy I think.
It whisks the dust
From Grandma's mop
And sends it flying
Into the sky.
Just when I think
The wind will stop,
It lifts my hat
And sends it spinning
Along the path.

Chuck's Best Pal

Chuck is at a big ranch.

The ranch is in the West.

At sun-up, Chuck straps on his chaps.

Chuck jumps on Champ's back.

Then Champ gallops across the hills.

The cows must get fresh grass.

Chuck and Champ will help them.

Past a pond and up a hill gallops Champ.

Champ stops galloping.

Chuck jumps down and rubs Champ's leg.

Champ has a bump on his leg.

"I must not let him run," thinks Chuck.

Back to the ranch plods Chuck.

Champ limps along with him.

The wind gusts across the hill.

Chuck stops and sniffs.

Yippy!" yells Chuck. "I smell flapjacks."

The chuckwagon is down the hill.
"I will rest and get my lunch
at the chuckwagon.
Champ can rest too."

Chuck pats his best pal.
"I will fix Champ's leg
when I get him back to the ranch.
Then Champ can rest.
When his leg is well, Champ
and I will gallop across the hills."

A Dandy Lunch

Rusty Fox sits in his den.
"My, my! I wish I had a rabbit sandwich.
I must get a rabbit.
A rabbit sandwich is such a dandy lunch."

Off into the thicket runs Rusty Fox.
"I will set a trap.
Rabbits run along this path.
I will get my rabbit sandwich."
Rusty Fox rubs his tummy.

Rusty sets his trap and runs
into the long grass.
"When a rabbit steps into my trap,
I will yank on this string.
Then I will get my lunch."
Rusty sits down.
The string is on the grass.
The sun is hot and
Rusty fans himself.
Rusty sits
and sits.

"I must check that trap.
If a rabbit has spotted my trap,
I must fix it."
Rusty runs to his trap.
A rabbit hops along the path.
The rabbit spots the fox.
It hops quickly into the long grass.

Rusty bends down to check the trap.
As the fox steps into the trap,
the rabbit yanks the string.

Bang! Rusty is in the trap.
The rabbit grins.
"Rusty Fox will not get a rabbit
with that trap!"

Rusty Fox limps back to his den.
"I still wish I had a rabbit sandwich,"
thinks Rusty sadly.
"A rabbit sandwich is such a dandy lunch!"